Lydia Crook

CHRISTMAS PAPER PLAY

Play, Make,
Decorate!

IVY KIDS

THIS BOOK BELONGS TO

....

HOW TO USE THIS BOOK

Here are some items you may need for the
activities in this book:

STRING

COLOURED PENCILS

GLUE

DRINKING STRAWS

STICKY TAPE

SCISSORS

And here is a key for the dashed lines you'll
see throughout this book:

— — — — — — —   — — — — — —
   CUT LINE   FOLD LINE

CHRISTMAS PAPER PLAY

First published in the UK in 2015 by

Ivy Press

210 High Street

Lewes

East Sussex BN7 2NS

United Kingdom

www.ivypress.co.uk.

ISBN: 978-1-78240-247-3

This book was conceived, designed and produced by

Ivy Press

CREATIVE DIRECTOR   Peter Bridgewater

PUBLISHER   Susan Kelly

EDITORIAL DIRECTOR   Tom Kitch

MANAGING EDITOR   Hazel Songhurst

COMMISSIONING EDITOR   Georgia Amson-Bradshaw

ART DIRECTOR   Kim Hankinson

PROJECT EDITORS   Jacqui Sayers

Charlie Gardner

DESIGNER & ILLUSTRATOR   Lydia Crook

EDITORIAL ASSISTANT   Lucy Menzies

DESIGN ASSISTANT   Emily Hurlock

Printed in China

Origination by Ivy Press Reprographics

10 9 8 7 6 5 4 3 2 1

Distributed worldwide (except North America) by
Thames & Hudson Ltd, 181A High Holborn, London
WC1V 7QX, United Kingdom

MAKE A
PRETTY MINI
PAPER CHAIN

1. cut out all the strips along the pink dashed lines.

2. Take one strip and add glue to one shaded area. Loop the strip around to the other shaded area and press together.

3. Take another strip and repeat, but this time loop it through your first looped strip.

4. continue this process with the rest of the strips until you have a beautiful length of paper chain.

5. Now hang up your pretty mini paper chain!

SUPER SANTA
Optical Illusion!

It looks like
MAGIC!

All you will need is some glue

and a straw

Colour in the picture below, then turn over
the page to find out how to make it . . .

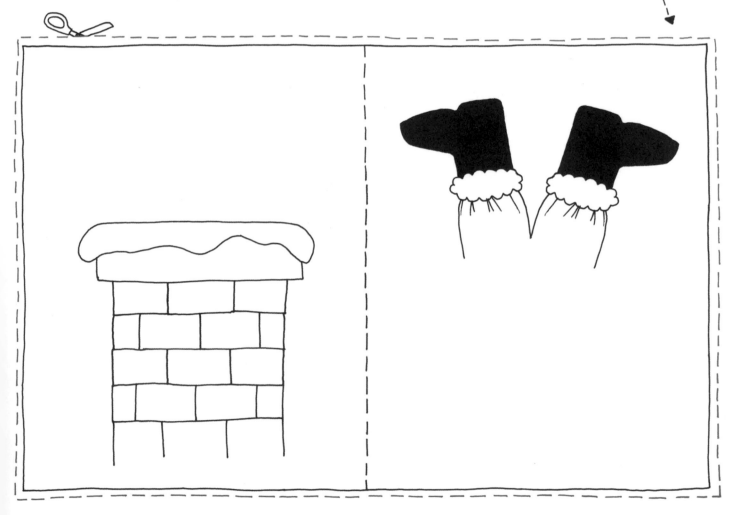

Cut out the box below along the pink dashed line.

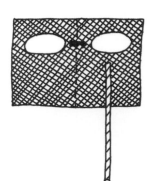 Put glue on the end of your straw and place it in the 'straw location' panel.

Add glue to the one half of the shaded area and then fold the paper in half along the central dashed line. Sandwich the straw between the two layers. Press down lightly to fix the straw in place.

 Once the glue has dried, place the straw between the palm of your hands and roll it. Watch what happens to super Santa!

This is your central fold line

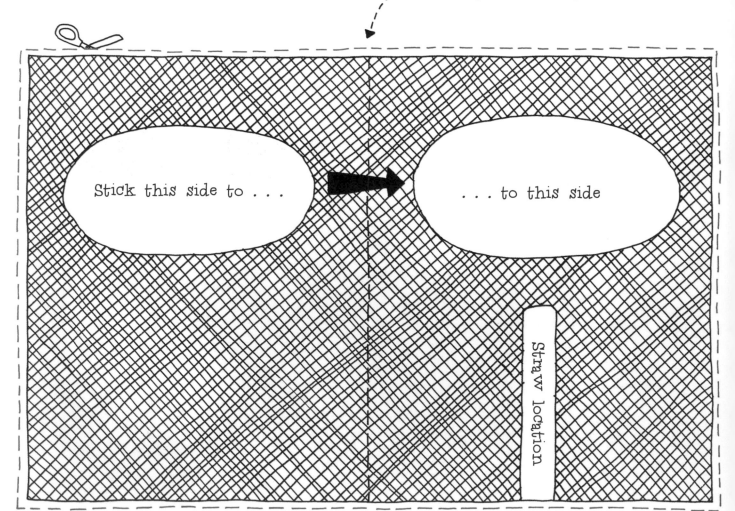

Stick this side to . . .   . . . to this side

Straw location

Fabulous Festive
Fingerprints

Create a spectacular festive scene using your fingers and some imagination.

SLEDGE

SNOWMAN

REINDEER

ANGEL

All you need is coloured ink pads, a pen and your hands! Copy the fingerprints above and create your own Christmas scene below.

MAKE AND DECORATE YOUR VERY OWN PAPER CHRISTMAS TREE . . .

 Colour in the decorations on the opposite page. Don't forget to colour in the reverse side too. If you like, you can add some glitter or something sparkly.

 Carefully cut out the trees and decorations along the pink dashed lines.

 Glue your coloured-in decorations onto all the sides of your trees.

 Slot together the two decorated trees. (Sing or hum a festive tune while you do this bit!)

 As a finishing touch, add either the star or the angel to the top of the tree that has the notch. Finally, stand it up and admire it.

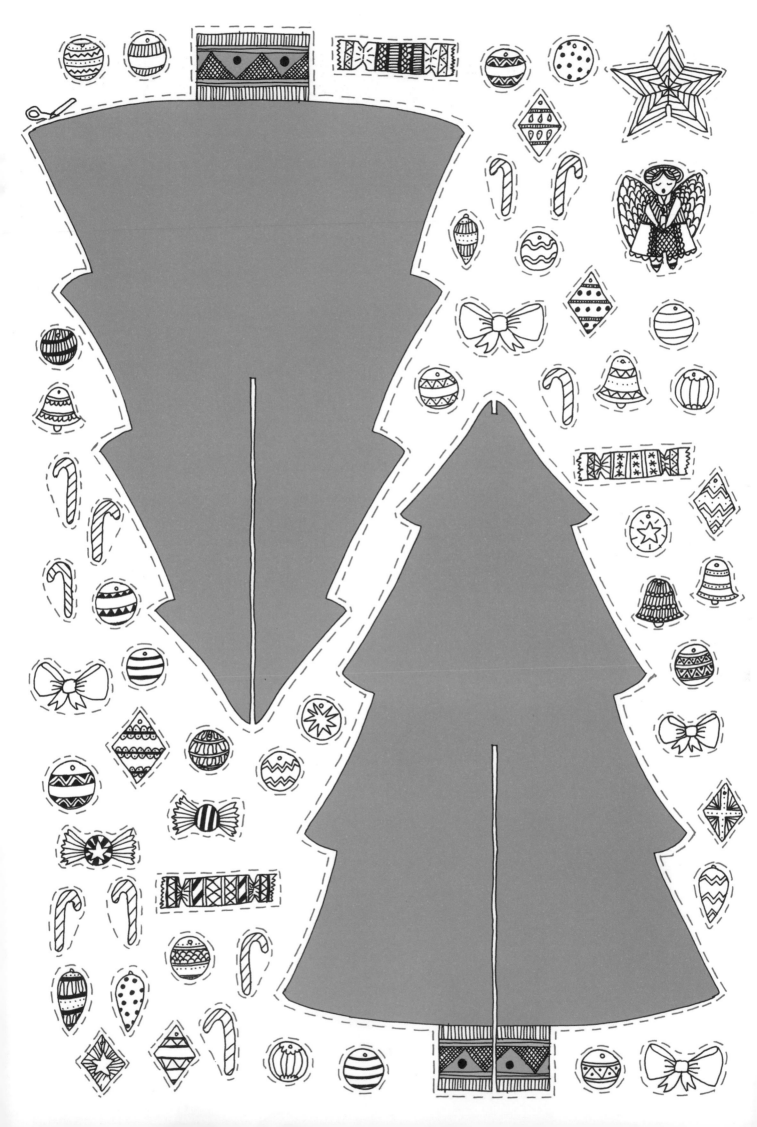

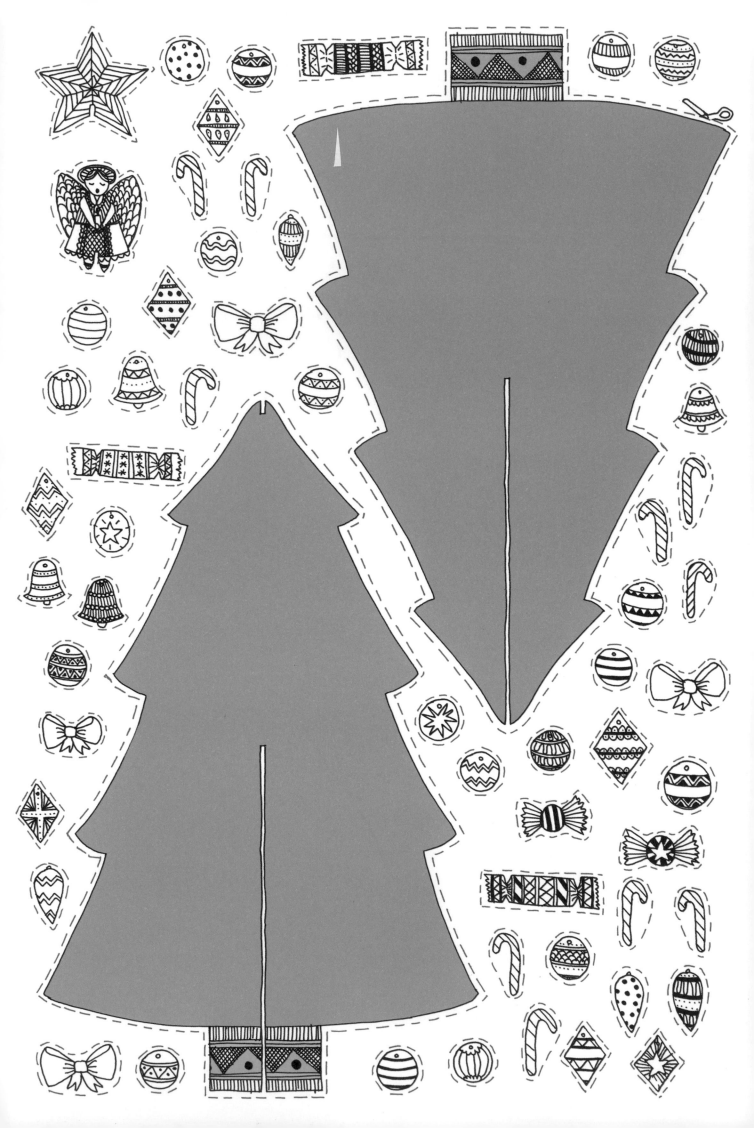

CHRISTMAS FAMILY PORTRAIT

Colour and draw the faces on this Christmas family portrait scene. They could even be the faces of your friends or family!

This portrait is of the

_ _ _ _ _ _ _ _ _ _ _ _ _ _ _

family

Create an amazing  **ADVENT CALENDAR** out of the next couple of pages

HOW TO MAKE YOUR ADVENT CALENDAR:

I) Colour in the the next four pages. They will make up your Advent calendar.

2) Add some fun and festive illustrations to the pictures page where instructed. You will see these when you open your Advent windows.

3) Cut out the pages along the pink dashed lines. _ _ _ _ _ _ _

4) Take the numbers page and carefully cut around the windows along the pink dashed lines. As this can be a little fiddly, you may need help from an adult using a craft knife.

5) Add a little glue around the edge of the pictures page — shown as a shaded area — and then stick the numbers page on top with the numbers facing up.

6) Add your name to the back of the calendar so that everyone knows it's yours.

7) Display your calendar somewhere special. Every day, over the month of Advent, you can open a window.

14

10

7

16

1

15

2

6

11

9

4

22

17

20

5

24

12

18

3

19

8

21

13

23

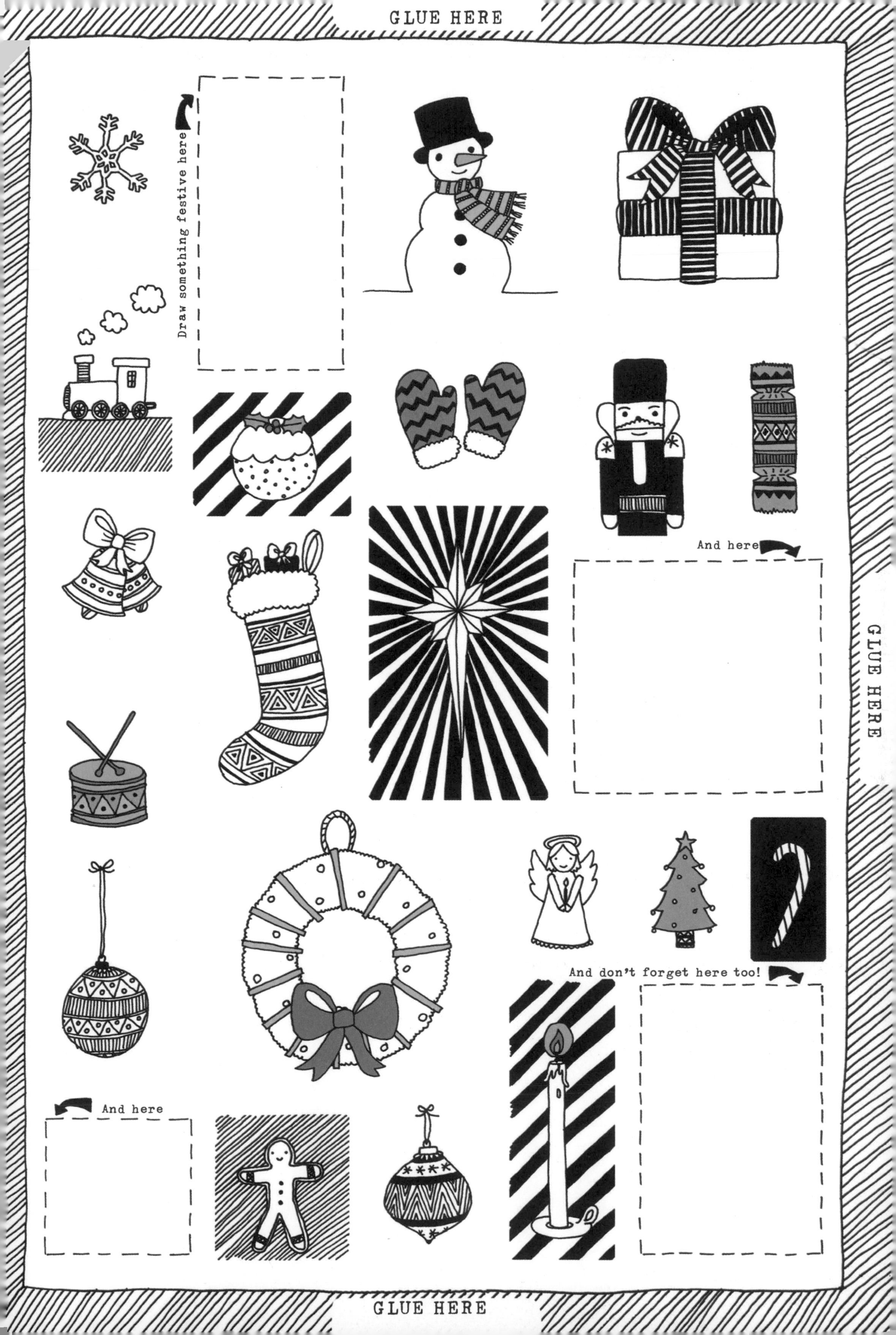
GLUE HERE
Draw something festive here
And here
GLUE HERE
And don't forget here too!
And here
GLUE HERE

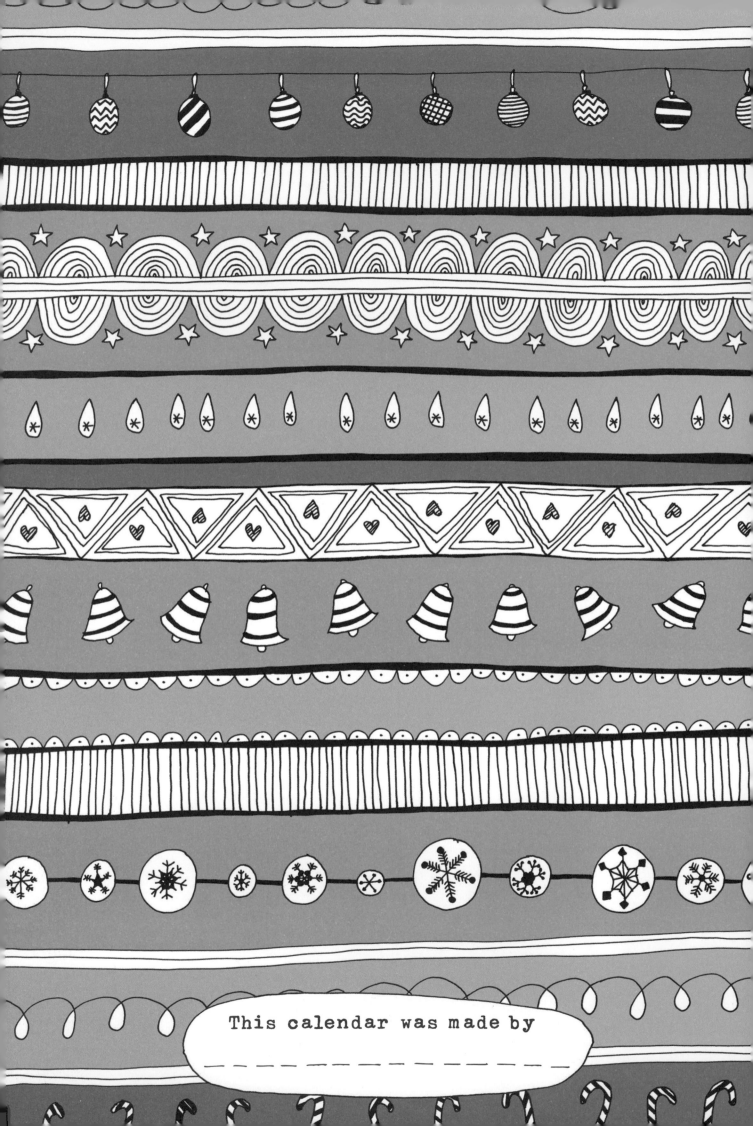

This calendar was made by

Winter Leaf Art

Collect some fallen leaves – the stranger the shapes, the better. Place the leaves underneath this page. Scribble over the page with a crayon and see a beautiful winter leaf artwork appear! **TIP**: Try not to let your leaves move about while you're scribbling!

The leaves I used to make my winter leaf art were :

. . . .

. . . .

Dear Santa . . .

Make your letter and envelope to Santa out of this page

1. Cut out along the pink dashed line.

2. Add glue to the two shaded areas on this side.

From:

Santa Claus
1 Reindeer Lane
The North Pole

With the stripy side facing up, fold the two side flaps inwards along the black dashed lines.

3.

4. Fold the bottom flap up, sticking it on top of the side flaps. Finally, fold the top flap down. When the letter is in the envelope, secure the top flap down with some sticky tape.

Cut out and fill in the letter, pop it in the envelope and post to Santa.

Dear Santa,
My name is . . . .
and I am . . . . . . years old.
I have been very . . . .
this year. I helped fix . . . .
and I even cleaned . . . .
I know you are very busy
but if you have time I would
like a . . . . , a . . . . . . , a . . . . . . ,
' . . . .
a . . . . and a
. . . . for Christmas.
I promise to leave you and
the reindeer a treat when
you come and visit.
Love,
. . . .

Rip
this
page
into
lots
and
lots
of
little
pieces
to
make
snow!

STICK A STOCKING

Decorate the stockings below and then follow the instructions on the next page . . .

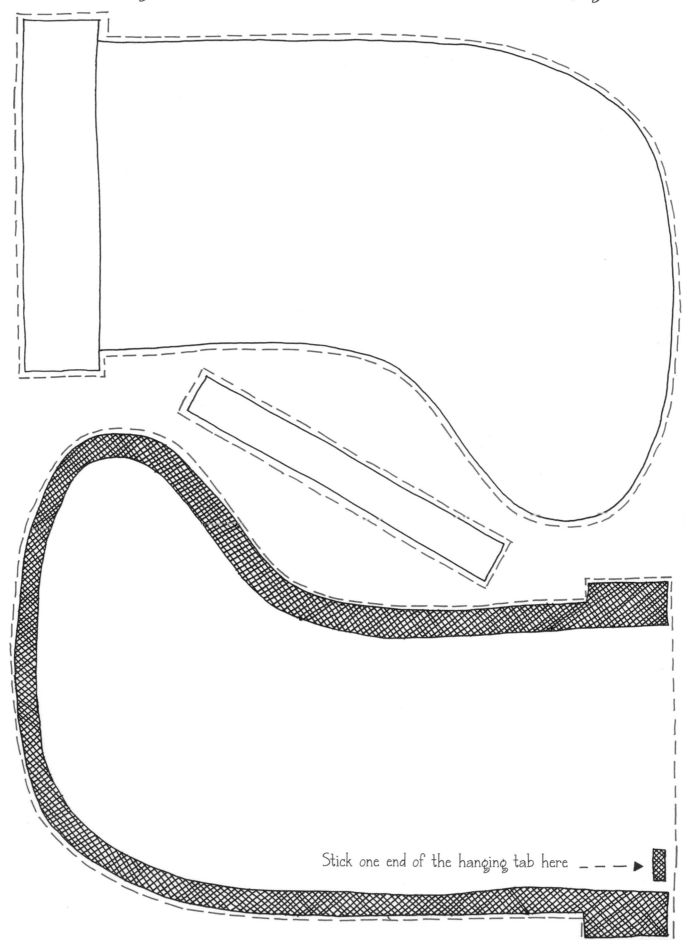

Stick one end of the hanging tab here _ _ _ ▶

HOW TO MAKE YOUR PAPER STOCKING:

Cut along the pink dashed lines. Add glue to one of the stocking's shaded areas and sandwich them together. Add glue to the shaded areas on the hanging tab and glue the ends inside your stocking. Hang up your stocking and wait for presents!

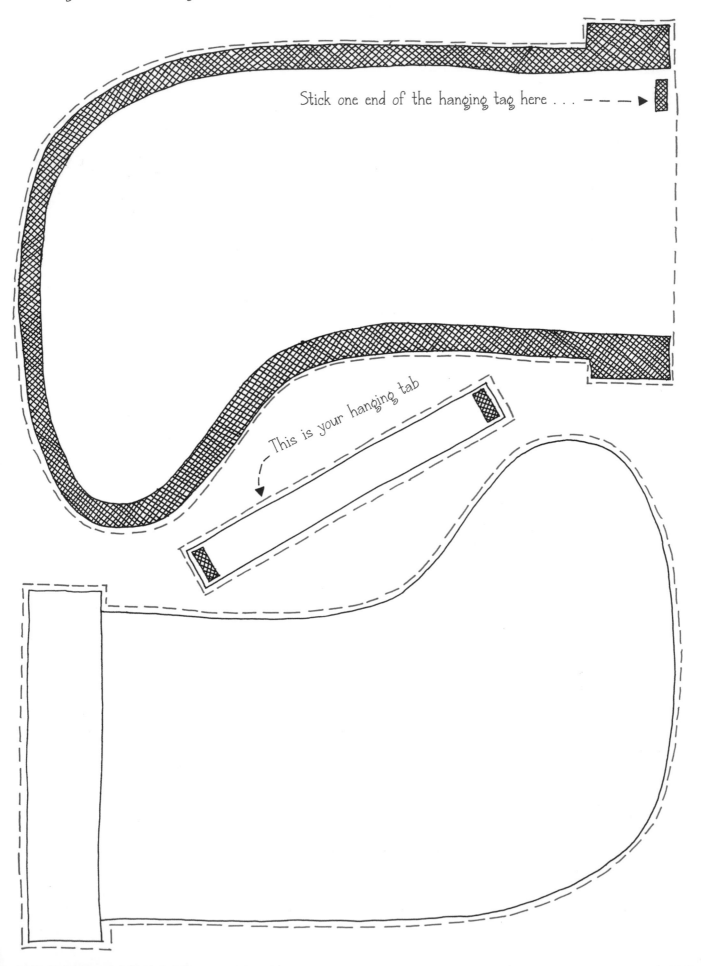

Stick one end of the hanging tag here . . . - - - ►

This is your hanging tab

Colour in this Christmas tree with your eyes closed!

Make Finger Puppet Friends

out of the next page

 Colour in the characters on the next page.

 Cut them out along the pink dashed lines.

 Add glue to the shaded areas on the front of each character.

 Wrap around your finger and join the shaded areas together so they stick.

check that you put glue
on both (front/back)
shaded areas

Don't forget to colour in this side too . . .

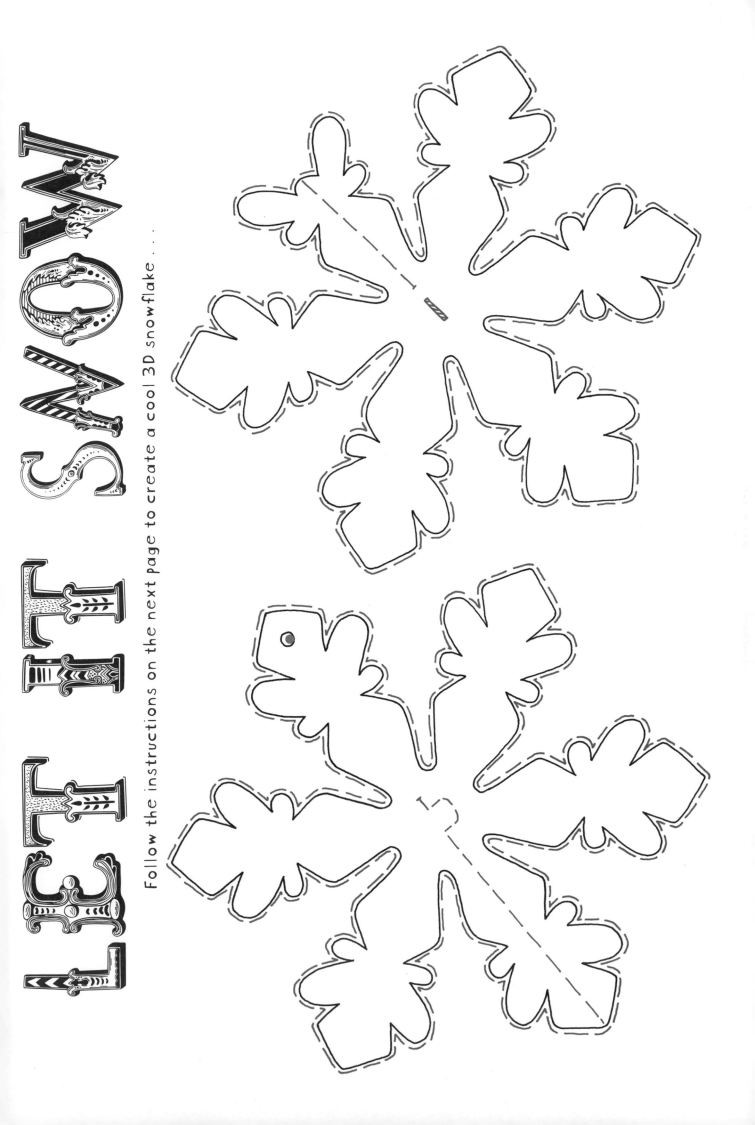

LET IT SNOW

Follow the instructions on the next page to create a cool 3D snowflake . . .

HOW TO MAKE YOUR SNOWFLAKE:

Cut out the snowflakes along the pink dashed lines. Carefully cut along the dashed lines from the edge to the centre. Ask an adult helper to cut out the slot in the centre of the top snowflake and the top hole. Slot the pieces together and push the tab through the slot. Thread some thin ribbon through the top hole, hang up and admire!

HAVE A SNOWBALL FIGHT WITH THIS PAGE

Rip this page in half, screw up the pieces and use them to have a snowball fight!

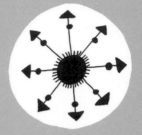

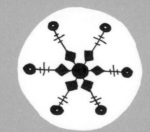

CHRISTMAS DOT-TO-DOT

Don't forget to colour it in when you've completed the picture!

Fold an amazing FLEXA FLAKE out of this page - - - - ▶

---

1. Cut out the shape along the pink dashed lines.

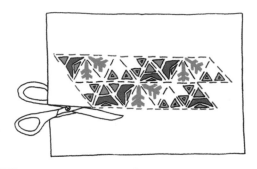

---

2. Fold all the black dashed lines both ways – forwards and backwards.

---

3. Flip over and add glue to the large top shaded area. Fold down.

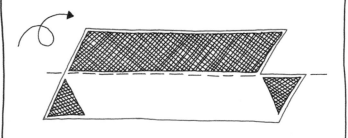

---

4. Fold the Flexa Flake in half (the left side backwards) along the line shown below.

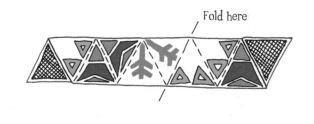

Fold here

---

5. Fold the Flexa Flake again along the line shown here. Make sure all the same pattern is facing upwards.

Fold here

---

6. Add glue to one shaded area and stick it onto the other shaded area to make a hexagon.

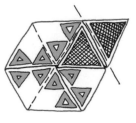

HOW TO FLEX YOUR
FLEXA FLAKE

↓

Pinch and fold down
the outer edges of the
hexagon to make a
three-pointed star.

↓

Now open out the
star from the centre
to make a hexagon
again, and watch
the pattern change.

↓

↓

↓

↓

↓

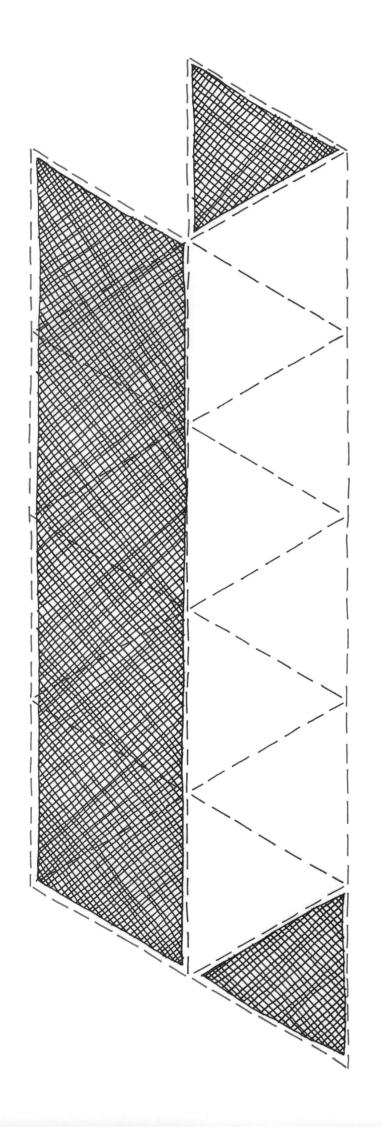

Paper Partridge

Create a spectacular
paper partridge out of
this page . . .

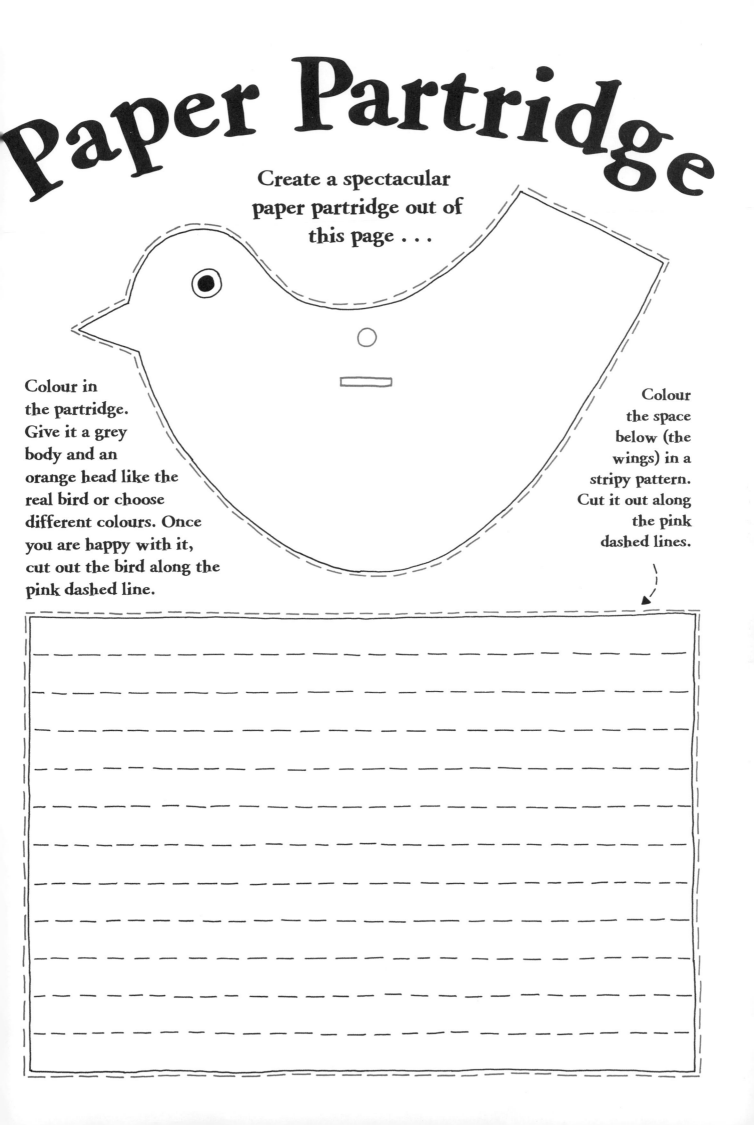

Colour in
the partridge.
Give it a grey
body and an
orange head like the
real bird or choose
different colours. Once
you are happy with it,
cut out the bird along the
pink dashed line.

Colour
the space
below (the
wings) in a
stripy pattern.
Cut it out along
the pink
dashed lines.

Ask an adult to cut out the two small holes and the slot in the bird's body. Now concertina-fold (that's a swish way of saying zig-zag!) the wings and post them through the slot. Fan the wings out evenly on both sides and thread string or ribbon through the hole. You could decorate your Christmas tree or bedroom with it.

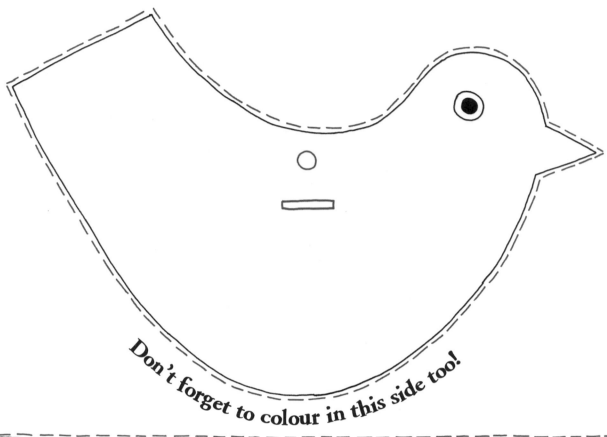

Don't forget to colour in this side too!

MAGIC PICTURE SWITCHER

Instructions on next page...

How to make your Magic Picture Switcher:

1. Ask an adult to cut along the pink dashed line with a craft knife to make a flap. Fold to the right.

2. Fold the left column of numbers to the centre...

3. ...and again.

4. Pop a piece of sticky tape onto the projecting number 1 flap. Flip it over...

5. ...and fold the flap to the right, fixing it to the number 1 flap next to it. All six squares should have a number 1 on them.

6. Now cut out all the pictures on the next page along the pink dashed lines.

7. Add glue to the back of the picture squares with the number 1 on them and stick them to the number 1 squares on your Magic Picture Switcher.

8. Fold the switcher in half towards you then pull either side of the centre to reveal the six number 2 squares. Now stick the number 2 pictures in position.

9. Now fold and repeat with the number 3 pictures and number 4 pictures.

How to use your Magic Picture Switcher

With picture 4 showing on your Magic Picture Switcher, fold it in half towards you then pull either side of the centre to reveal picture 3. Repeat folding and separating to make picture 2 appear . . . and so on. It's magic!

Do some Christmassy doodles on these baubles . . .

How to make your snowman and snowballs:

1 Cut out the snowman pieces on the opposite page along the pink dashed line. — — — — — — — — — — — — — — —

2 Colour in to make a groovy snowman. You could even draw a Christmas scene behind him.

3 Carefully cut out the shaded areas to make his mouth and tummy.

4 Fold in the sides along the black dashed lines and stand up your snowman. Use the sides as support.

5 Cut out the snowballs and score cards on the next page. Screw up the snowballs. You are now ready to play Feed the Snowman!

How to play Feed The Snowman (two players):

1 Place your snowman on a long table, about a metre from where you are sitting or standing.

2 Take it in turns to throw the snowballs (two balls per turn) through the snowman's mouth or tummy. If you get any through, you score points.

3 Write down your score as you play. The player with the most points wins!

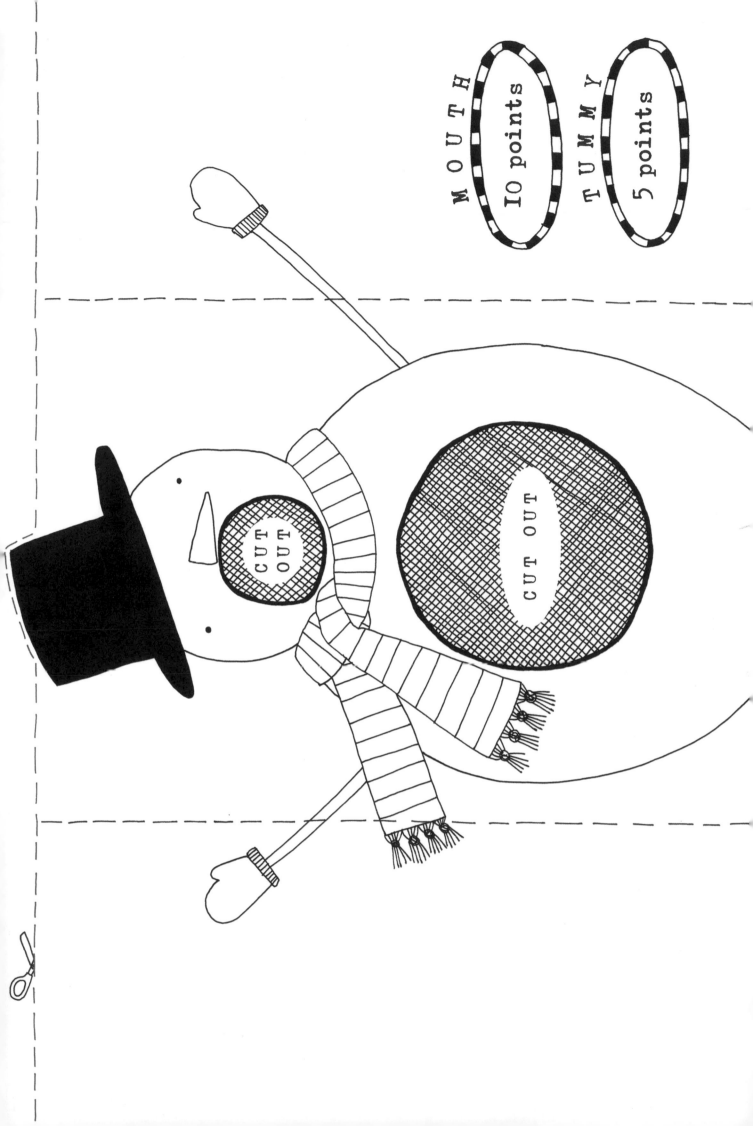

MOUTH
10 points

TUMMY
5 points

CUT OUT

CUT OUT

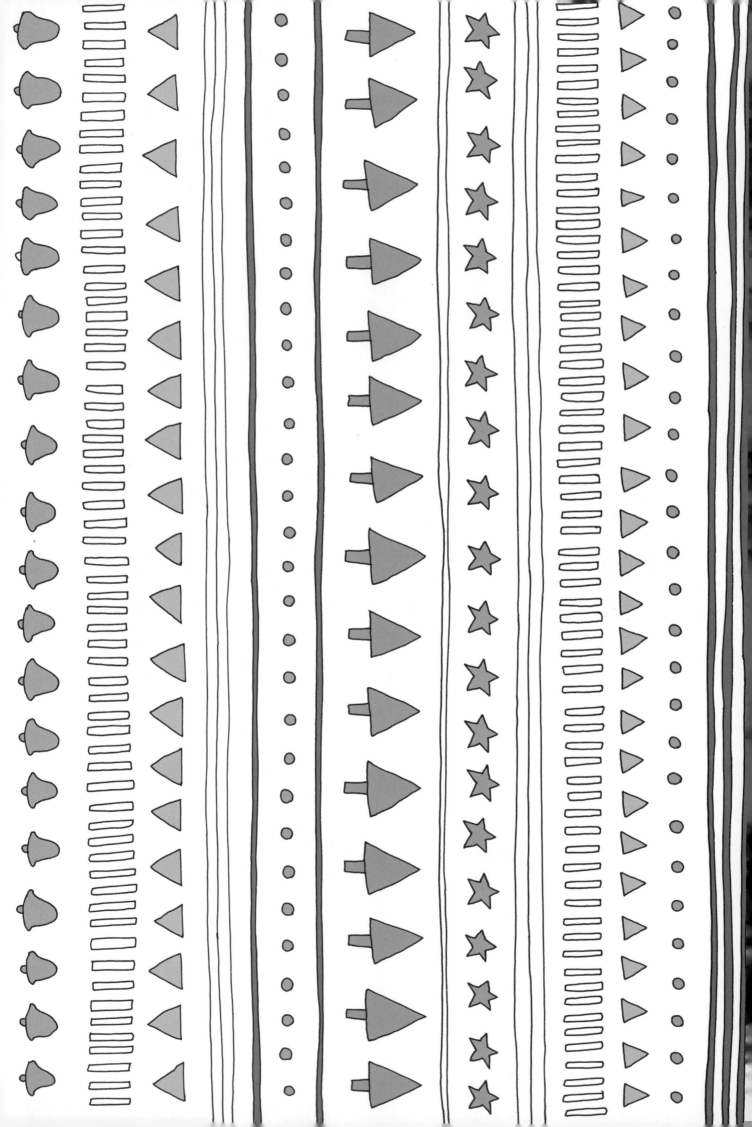

These are your
score cards

Cut out these squares and screw them up to make
snowballs. Each player gets two snowballs per turn.

PLAYER'S NAME

▶

TURN ▶

I

2

3

4

5

FINAL
SCORE

GAME ONE

PLAYER'S NAME

▶

TURN ▶

I

2

3

4

5

FINAL
SCORE

GAME TWO

Can you find all the hidden objects in this picture?

Items to find:

- [ ] 2 lollipops
- [ ] A stocking
- [ ] 2 bells
- [ ] A woolly hat
- [ ] A present
- [ ] 5 gold rings
- [ ] A teddy bear
- [ ] A carrot
- [ ] A robin
- [ ] A bow tie

WHAT'S YOU

Splodge paint on this side of the page, shut the book and then open it again . . . . .

R SPLODGE?

Can you make your splodge into something Christmassy? Maybe it's a reindeer or even an elf? What can you see in your splodge?

TANGRAM

Can you create these silhouettes below with the shapes from the next page?

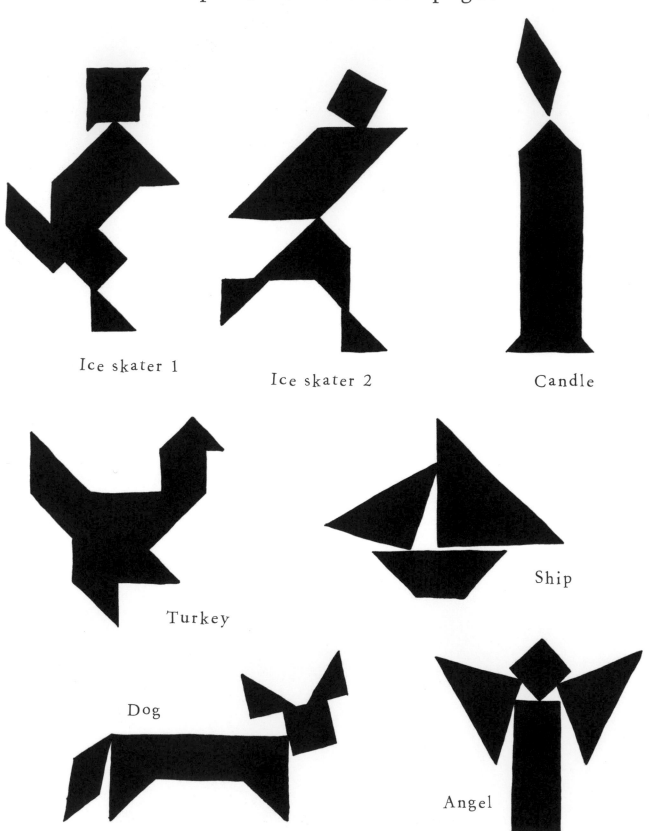

Ice skater 1

Ice skater 2

Candle

Turkey

Ship

Dog

Angel

CHALLENGE

Cut out the shapes below along the black lines:

2 big triangles, 1 medium triangle, 2 little triangles, 1 square, 1 parallelogram (a squashed rectangle).

Each silhouette is made out of ALL these shapes. The solutions are on the next page . . . no peeking! ▶

PAPER
JULEHJERTE

Pleated Christmas Heart

 Cut out the shapes below along the outer pink dashed lines (leaving the inner ones) and then follow the instructions on the next page . . .

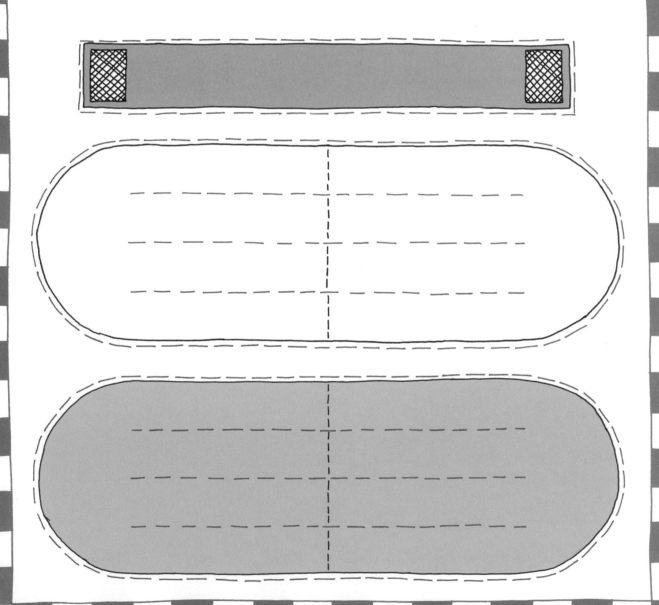

1. Fold the white and blue shapes in half along the black dashed lines and cut along the pink dashed line to make fingers! Open and fold the shapes the other way so the dashed lines are on the inside.

2. Take one outer white finger and slowly weave it into the blue fingers, threading through and over.

3. Thread each white finger in turn, making sure to go between and over (not under and on top) the other fingers.

4. As you get nearer the end, you might find it gets a little trickier to thread the paper fingers together.

5. Finally, add the orange handle by adding a bit of glue to the shaded area and sticking it inside your woven heart.

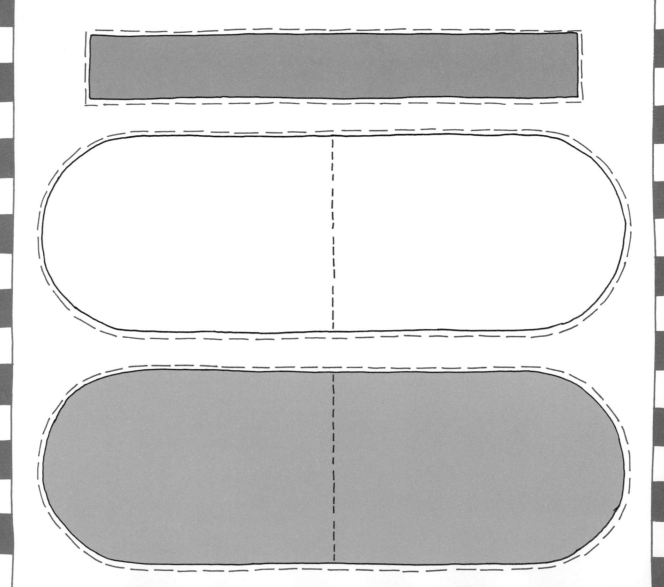

THE NEVER-ENDING STAR

use straight lines to join the dots in numerical order.

CHRISTMAS DRAWING GAME

1 Get a pencil or a pen. Then, carefully rip or cut out the list of instructions below.

2 Place this book, with this page open, on your head. Now look at the list of instructions you removed and, using a pencil, try to draw them on the opposite page without taking the book off your head. No peeking!

3 Once you have completed your list of instructions, take the book off your head and see how your drawing looks.

4 Now see what you've scored. Use the points system below:

2 POINTS if the tree touches the floor

2 POINTS if your stocking is touching your fireplace

1 POINT if your star touches your tree

1 POINT if your star is above your tree

1 POINT for every tree decoration that is ON your tree

1 POINT if your fireplace doesn't touch the tree (it's a fire hazard!)

1 POINT if you drew something decorative on your stocking

2 POINTS if your present is under your tree

INSTRUCTIONS

I. Draw a line for a floor.

2. Draw a Christmas tree. Add decorations if you like.

3. Draw a star on top of your tree.

4. Draw a fireplace next to the tree.

5. Draw a stocking hanging from your fireplace.

6. Draw a present below the tree.

My total score was

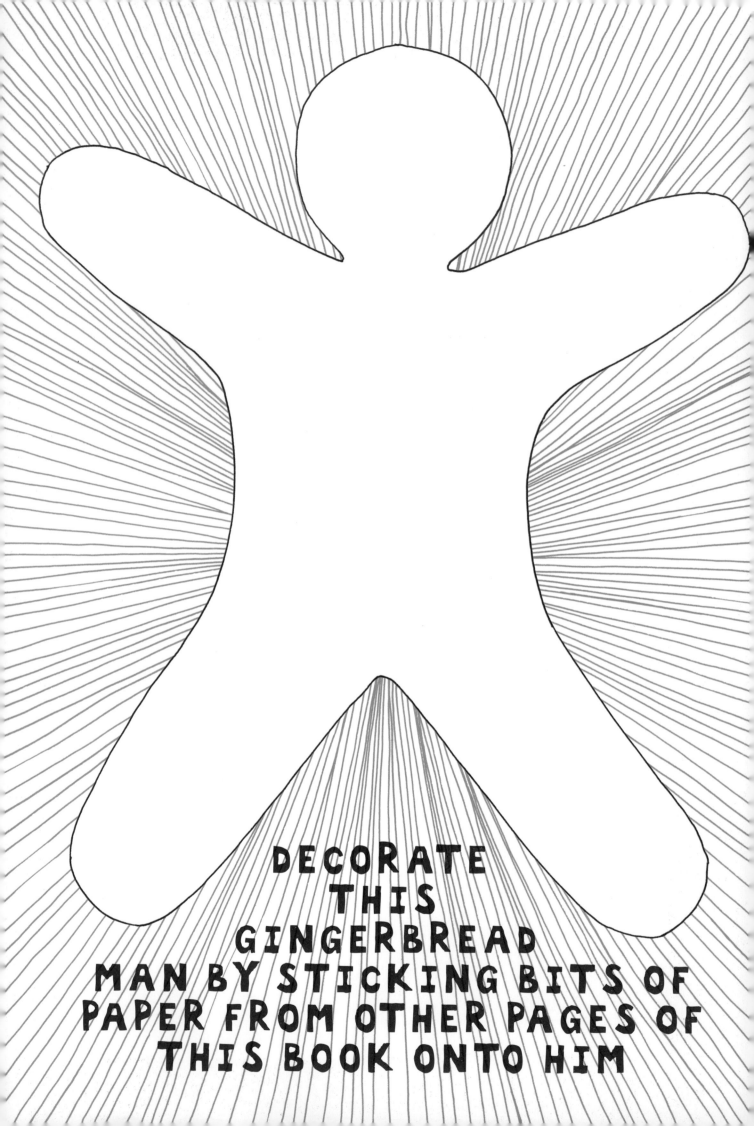

DECORATE
THIS
GINGERBREAD
MAN BY STICKING BITS OF
PAPER FROM OTHER PAGES OF
THIS BOOK ONTO HIM

HAVE A GAME OF CHRISTMAS CONSEQUENCES

PREPARING TO PLAY THE GAME (for 2-4 people)

1. Cut out the strips of paper below along the pink dashed lines.

2. Give each player a piece of paper and a pen or pencil.

3. Then read out loud the story instructions on the next page . . . .

Sit in a circle with the other players.

Each player writes
A MAN'S NAME
at the top of their piece of paper. Then each player folds over the paper a little (to hide the name) before passing it to the person to the left of them.

Each player then writes
A WOMAN'S NAME,
folds it over again and passes it to the person to the left.

Each player then writes
A PLACE NAME,
folds it over and passes it to the left.

Each player then writes
WHAT HE SAID TO HER,
folds it over and passes it left.

Each player then writes
WHAT SHE SAID TO HIM,
folds it over and passes it left.

Then each player writes what
THE CONSEQUENCE WAS . . .
(a short description of what happened next) folds it over and passes it left.

Finally, in turn, unfold the piece of paper and read out the stories!

TIP: you could use the back of the paper to have another go!

Photo
DRESS-UP
INSTRUCTIONS -----▶

cut out these funky photo props along the pink dashed lines. Glue a drinking straw on the backs where shown and use them as funny festive photo props.

STICK STRAW HERE

STICK STRAW HERE

STICK STRAW HERE

MAKE A
5-POINTED STAR
OUT OF THIS PAGE

Cut out the square below and follow the instructions on the next page . . .

1	2	3
Fold the square in half.	Lightly mark each corner with the letters as shown above. Bring corner C over so that it sits a third of the way down from the top of the A-D edge.	Fold corner D upwards between points C and F.
4	5	6
Bring point E over to point C so that it covers the D flap. Mark point G half way down the side, between points B and F.	Use scissors to make a cut from point G over to the point E and C. Keep the star (the lower section) and throw away the top half.	Open out the star. Taa daa! You have a beautiful 5-pointed star. Sticky tape some thread onto the back and hang up.

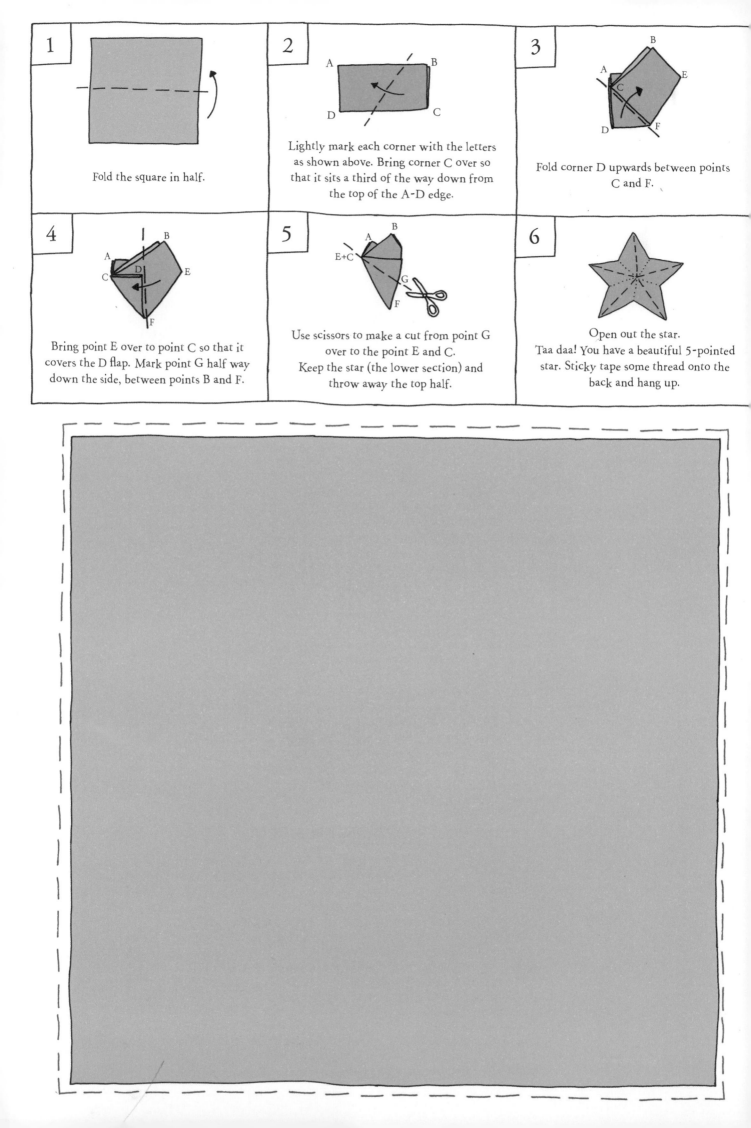

3D REINDEER

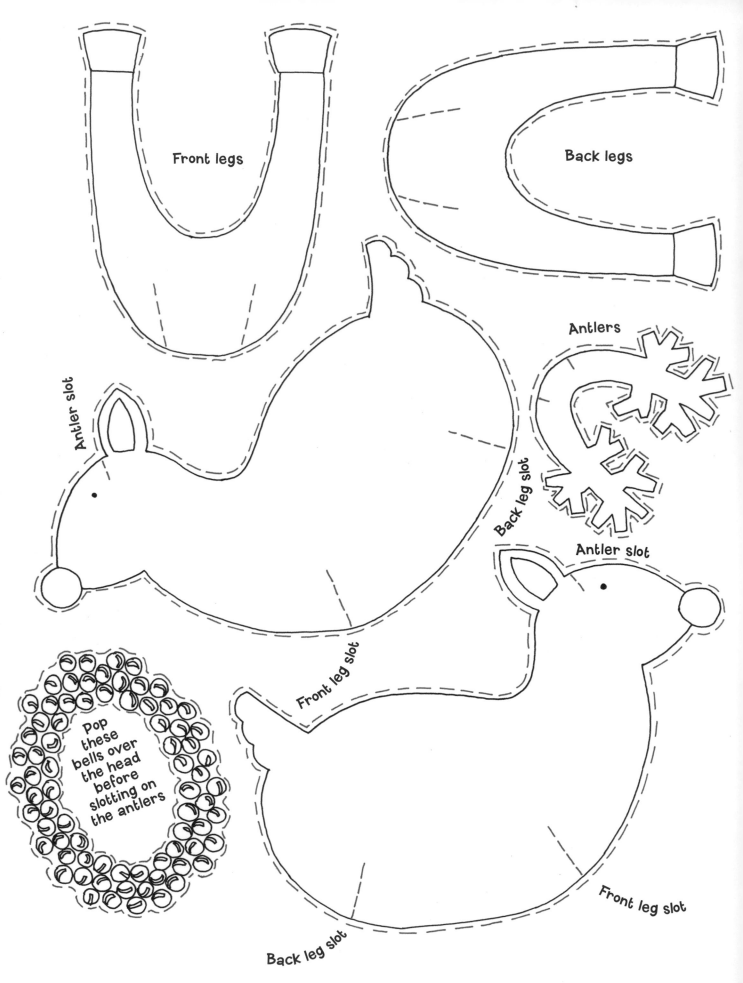

Front legs

Back legs

Antlers

Antler slot

Back leg slot

Antler slot

Front leg slot

pop these bells over the head before slotting on the antlers

Front leg slot

Back leg slot

Colour in and cut out all the pieces. Then slot them together where directed.

FESTIVE JIGSAW PUZZLE

DRAW A CHRISTMASSY SCENE IN THE SPACE BELOW. COLOUR IT IN AND THEN CUT IT OUT ALONG THE DASHED PINK LINE. CAREFULLY RIP THE PICTURE INTO 10-15 EVEN-SIZED PIECES. THEY CAN BE ANY SHAPE YOU WANT.

NOW . . . CAN YOU PUT YOUR PICTURE BACK TOGETHER AGAIN?

THE FASTEST TIME I PUT MY CHRISTMASSY JIGSAW BACK TOGETHER WAS . . . .

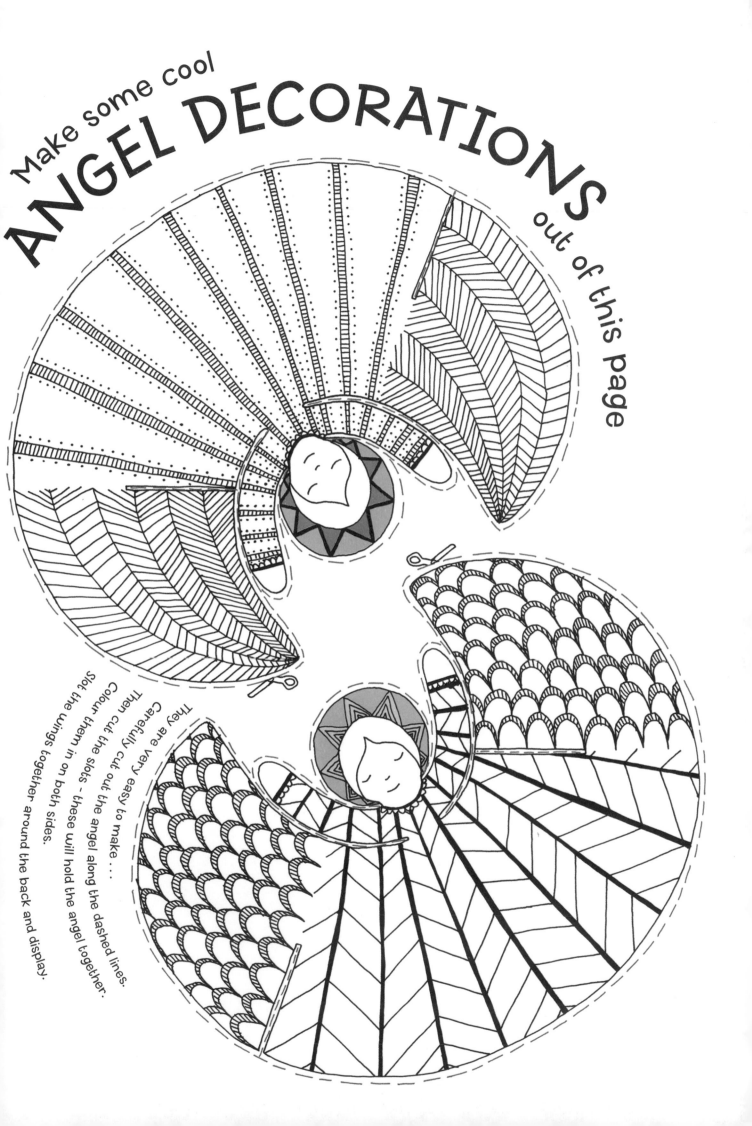

Make some cool
ANGEL DECORATIONS
out of this page

They are very easy to make ...
Carefully cut out the angel along the dashed lines.
Then colour them in on both sides.
Then cut out the slots – these will hold the angel together.
Slot the wings together around the back and display.

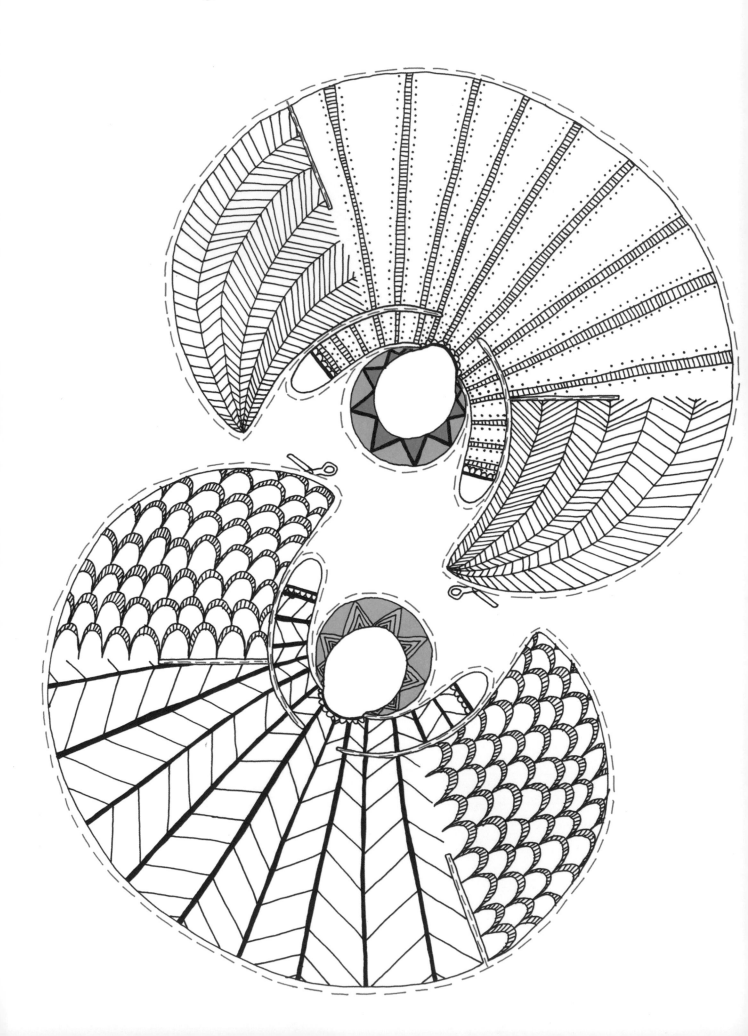

XMAS STENCILS

HOW TO USE THE STENCILS:

Cut out the four squares on the previous page. Carefully cut out the shaded areas in the middle, keeping the white areas whole. Place one of the stencils onto a large piece of paper. With paint, ink or a felt tip pen, use the stencil to draw the object. Repeat this process again just to the left of your first object. Continue until you have a lovely pattern all over the paper. You could use it for wrapping presents or cut it up to make gift tags.

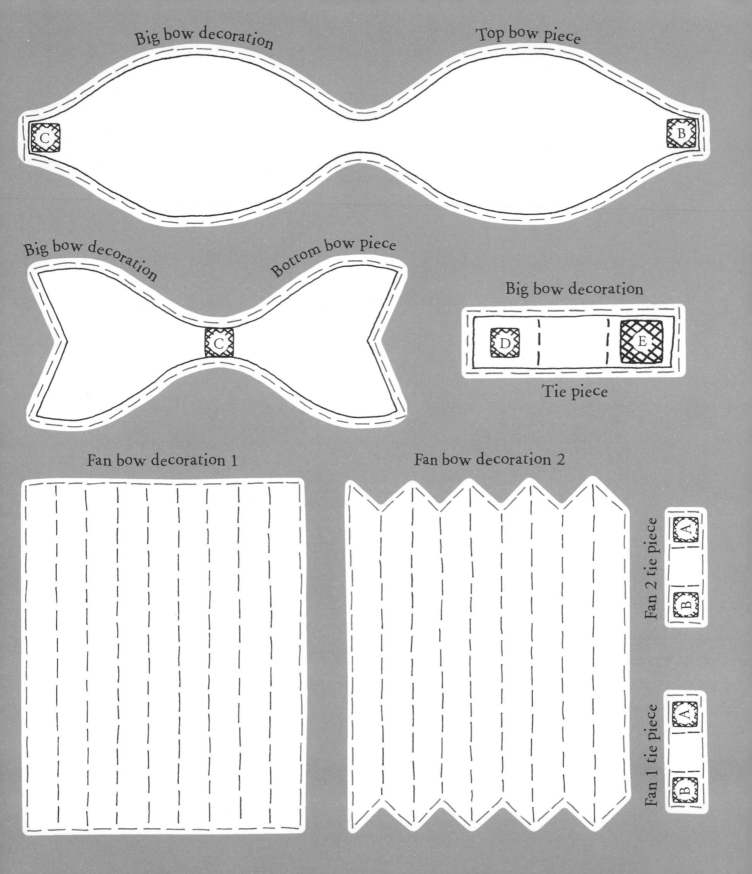

Big bow decoration — Top bow piece

Big bow decoration — Bottom bow piece

Big bow decoration — Tie piece

Fan bow decoration 1

Fan bow decoration 2

Fan 2 tie piece

Fan 1 tie piece

Beautiful Bows

Decorate the blank areas above and then follow the
instructions on the next page . . .

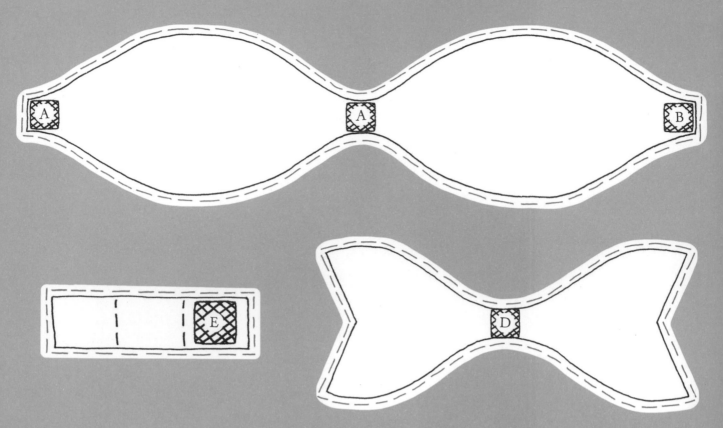

Decorate this side too and then carefully cut out the items along the pink dashed lines.

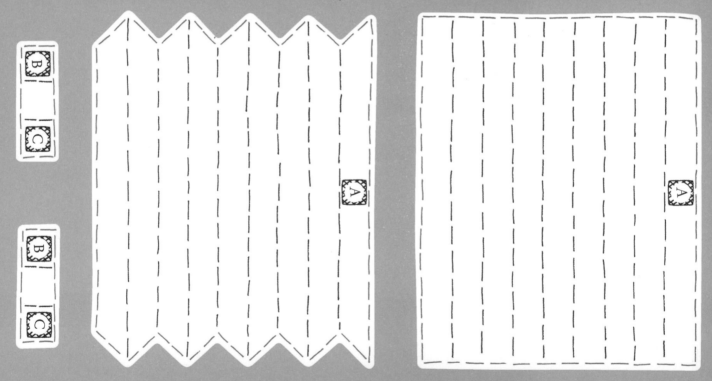

How to make a 'BIG BOW'

Fold and stick side A into the middle A of the top bow. Fold over side B and stick into the middle B. Glue the bottom bow onto the back of the top bow matching up glue points C. Stick the tie piece onto the bottom bow piece, matching up glue points D. Wrap the tie around the centre of the stuck together pieces. Glue points E together. Add a little glue onto the back of the bow and decorate a prezzie with it.

How to make a 'FAN BOW'

Concertina fold (zig-zag) one of your fan pieces. Wrap a fan tie piece around the centre on the folded decoration piece and glue in place matching glue areas A and B (this should hold the fan tightly in the middle). Add a little glue onto the back of the bow (glue point C) and decorate another prezzie with it. Fan out the ends to make it into a bow shape.

FESTIVE PAIRS GAME

CUT OUT THE PICTURES BELOW ALONG THE PINK DASHED LINES
AND FOLLOW THE INSTRUCTIONS ON THE NEXT PAGE

HOW TO PLAY

This is a great game for two players.

Mix up all the cut out cards and place them upside down in front of you.

Taking turns, flip over two cards chosen at random showing them to the other players.

If the pictures match, you have a pair. Pick your pair up and place them in front of you and take another go.

If your pictures do not match, turn them back over. It is now the next player's turn.

Once all the paired cards have been claimed it is the end of the game.

The winner is the player who found the most pairs.

Make some COOL CRACKERS out of the next page

How to make your

COOL CRACKERS

1. Cut out the crackers on the next page along the pink dashed lines. Don't forget to cut out the diamond shapes in the middle.

2. Decorate the blank cracker with pens, paints, glitter or whatever you fancy.

3. Fold all the black dashed lines forwards and backwards.

4. Roll up one of your crackers and add glue to the shaded tabs. Carefully stick the tabs onto the shaded areas on the inner side of your cracker.

5. Write a Christmas wish on a small square of paper and pop it into your cracker. You could even add some snow confetti from one of the other pages of this book.

6. Finally, pinch the diamond areas at each end inwards and secure in place with an elastic band or ribbon.
Repeat with the other cracker.

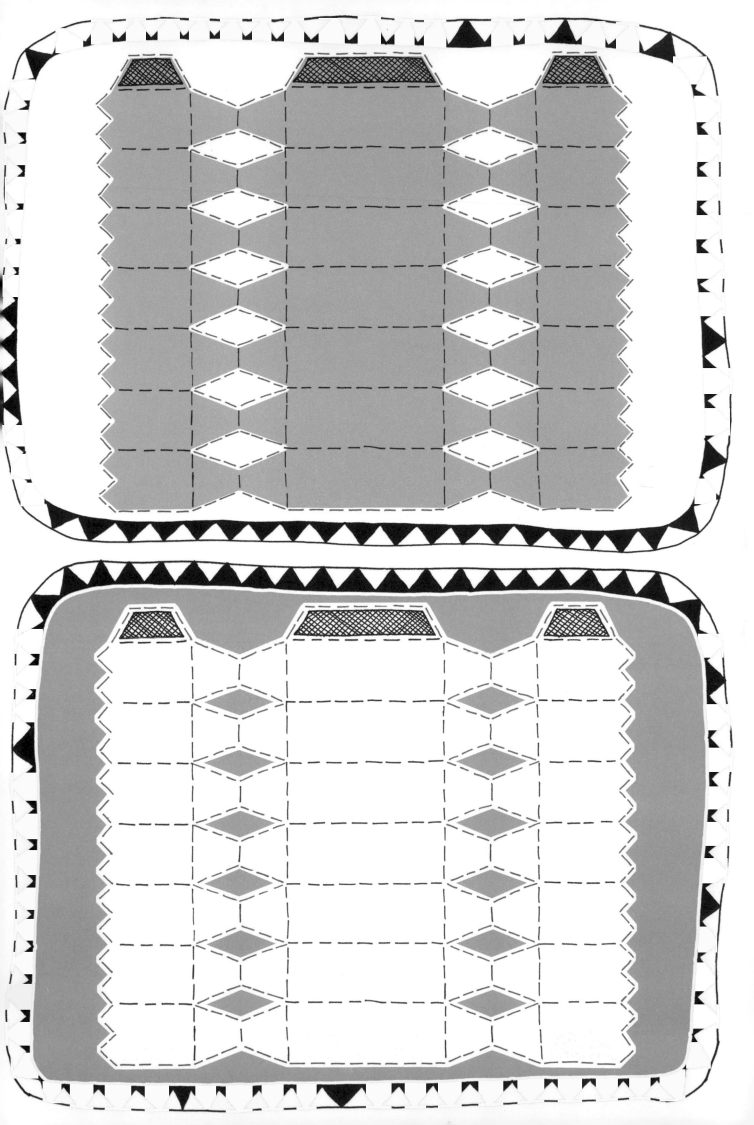

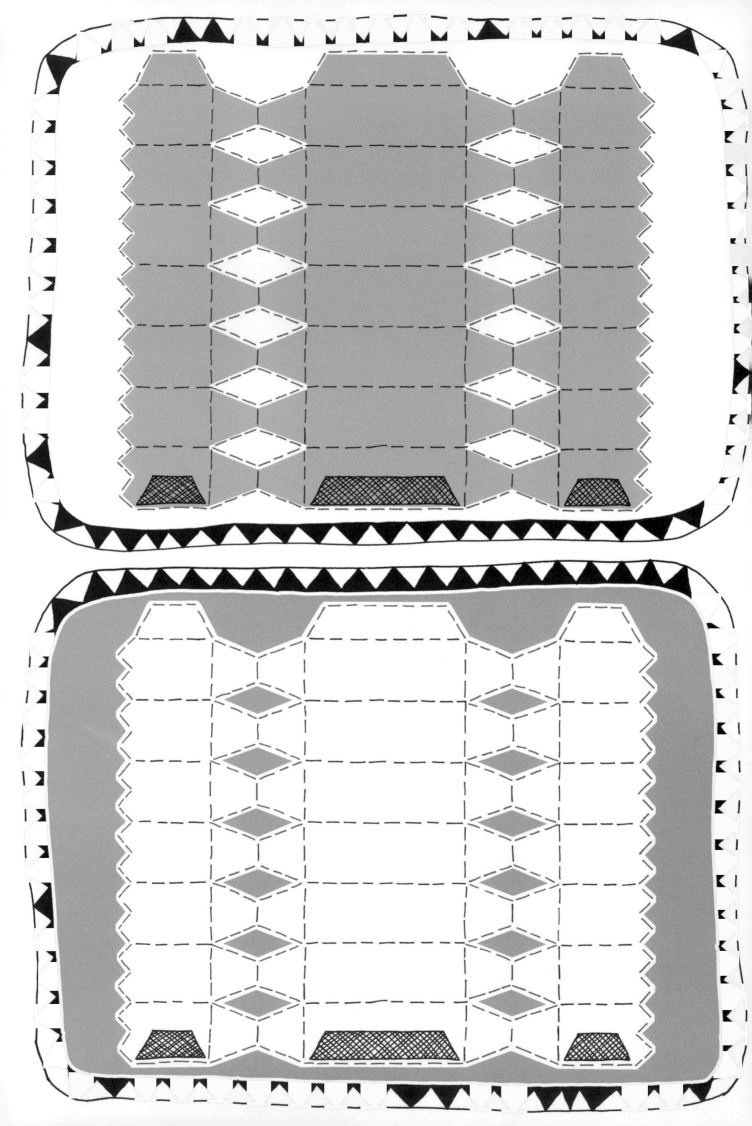

CHRISTMAS GARLAND

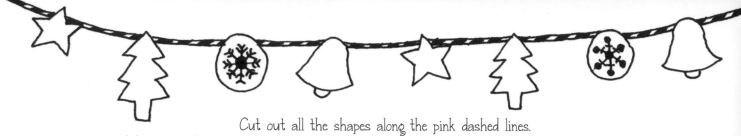

Cut out all the shapes along the pink dashed lines.
Measure and cut a piece of string or ribbon to your desired length and lay it out straight.
Place your shapes onto the string using the 'STRING' location areas as a guide, making them evenly spaced apart.
Secure in place with sticky tape. Hang up and admire your awesome Christmas garland.

The Bobbing Robin

tweet
TWEET

Create this fab origami bobbing robin. Cut out the square below and then follow the instructions overleaf...

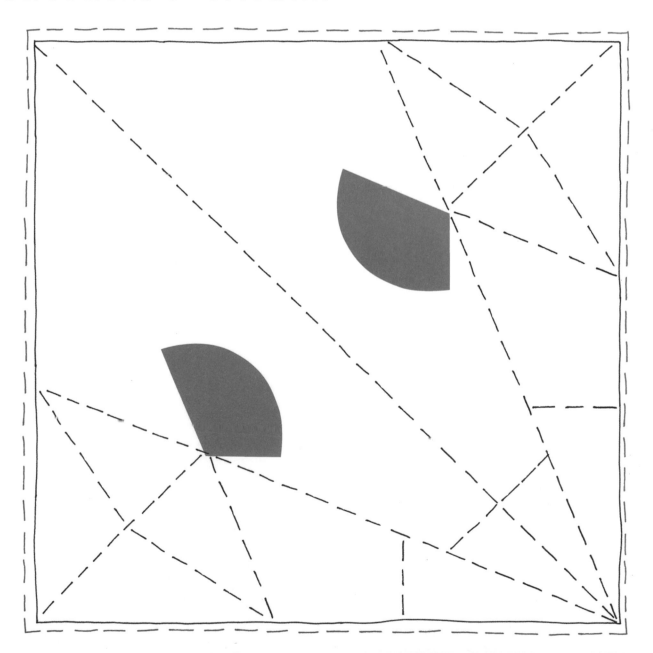

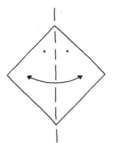

1. Fold in half along the dashed line and then open out again.

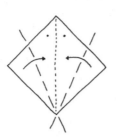

2. Fold in the two side corners to the central fold line.

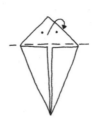

3. Fold the top corner over backwards.

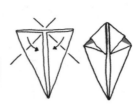

4. Fold in the top corners to meet the central fold.

5. Open these folded areas inside out and flatten using the dashed lines as a guide.

6. Fold up these corners to meet the folded/dashed line – these are your Robin's feet.

7. Fold the bottom point up to the centre and then back on itself to create a tail.

8. Fold the whole piece in half and then turn it around – your Robin should start to take shape.

9. Finally, fold the beak point inwards, pinching and creasing along the dashed lines.

To start your Robin bobbing...

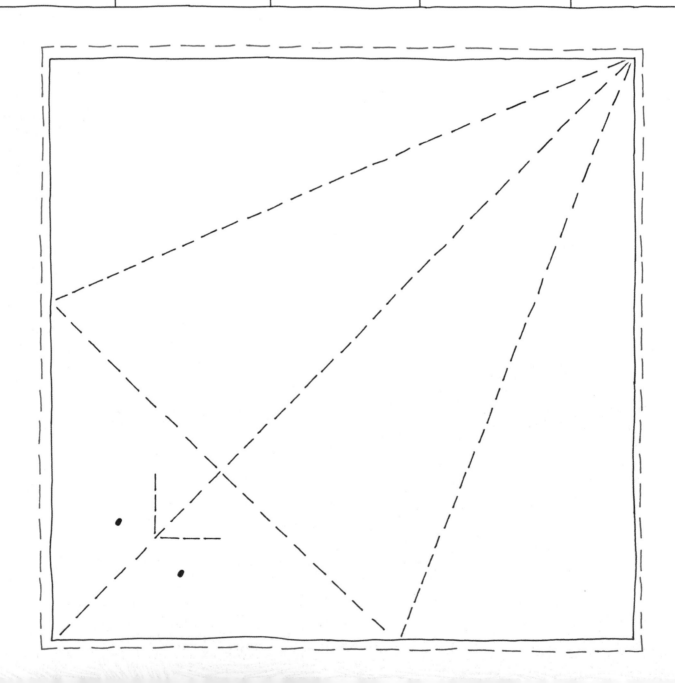

HOW NEATLY CAN YOU RIP THESE SHAPES OUT?

CHRISTMAS PAPER CHAIN

Make some cool Christmassy paper chains out of this page . . .

Ask an adult to help you cut out the strips of paper below along the pink dashed lines, and then follow the instructions on the next page . . .

How to make your Christmas paper chains:

Concertina fold one of your strips of paper along the black dashed lines.

Draw something Christmassy on the front, making sure there are some areas that go over the side folds (this is so your paper chain doesn't fall apart).

Cut out the shape. Unfold and ta-da! Your paper chain is complete.

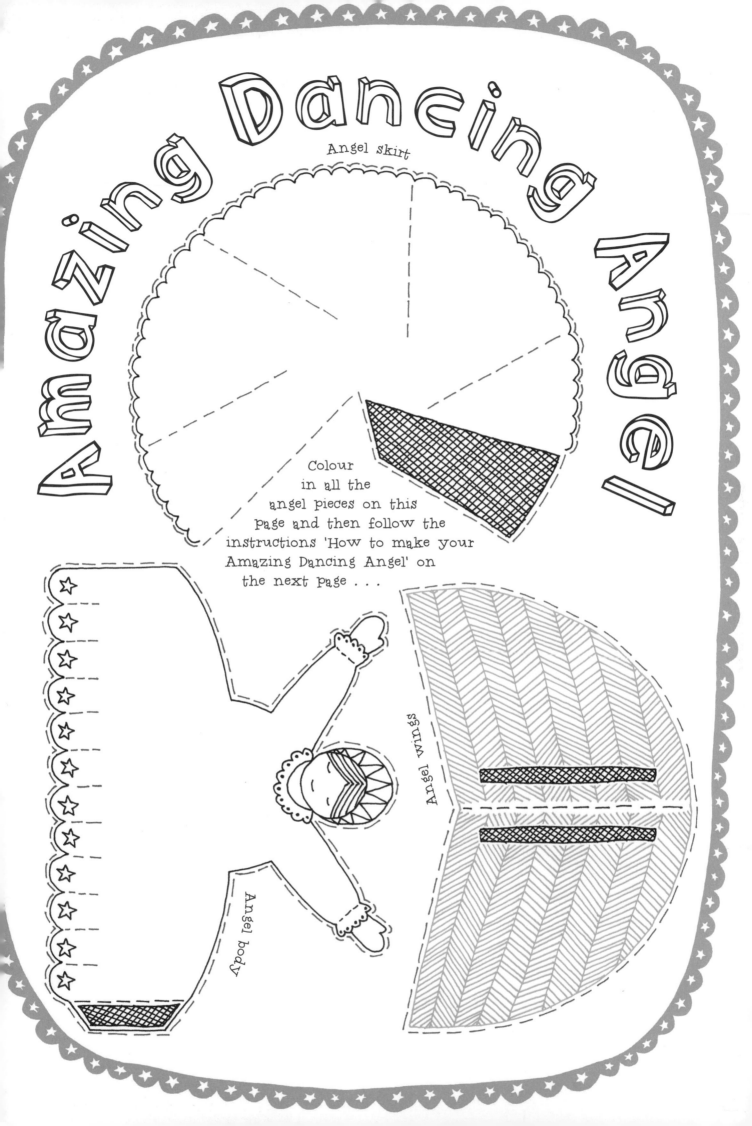

Amazing Dancing Angel

Angel skirt

Colour in all the angel pieces on this page and then follow the instructions 'How to make your Amazing Dancing Angel' on the next page . . .

Angel wings

Angel body

Colour in this side too!

How to make your Amazing Dancing Angel:

Carefully cut out all your angel pieces along the pink dashed lines, without forgetting the lines going into the skirt!

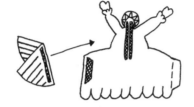

Add some glue to the shaded area of the wings and glue it onto the back of your angel body. Use the matching shaded area as a position guide.

Add glue to the side tab of your angel body. Wrap it around and secure in place. Add glue to the skirt glue tab. Wrap it around and secure in place. This should create a cone-type shape.

Glue the angel body onto the skirt using the star tabs.

Finally, when the glue is dry, pop your angel onto the tip of a pencil. Give it a gentle puff and watch her dance and spin.

CHRISTMAS COLOUR BY NUMBERS

Colour in the Christmas scene using these numbers and colours as a guide.

(1) RED   (2) ORANGE   (3) BLUE   (4) LIGHT GREEN

(5) DARK GREEN   (6) BROWN   (7) BLACK

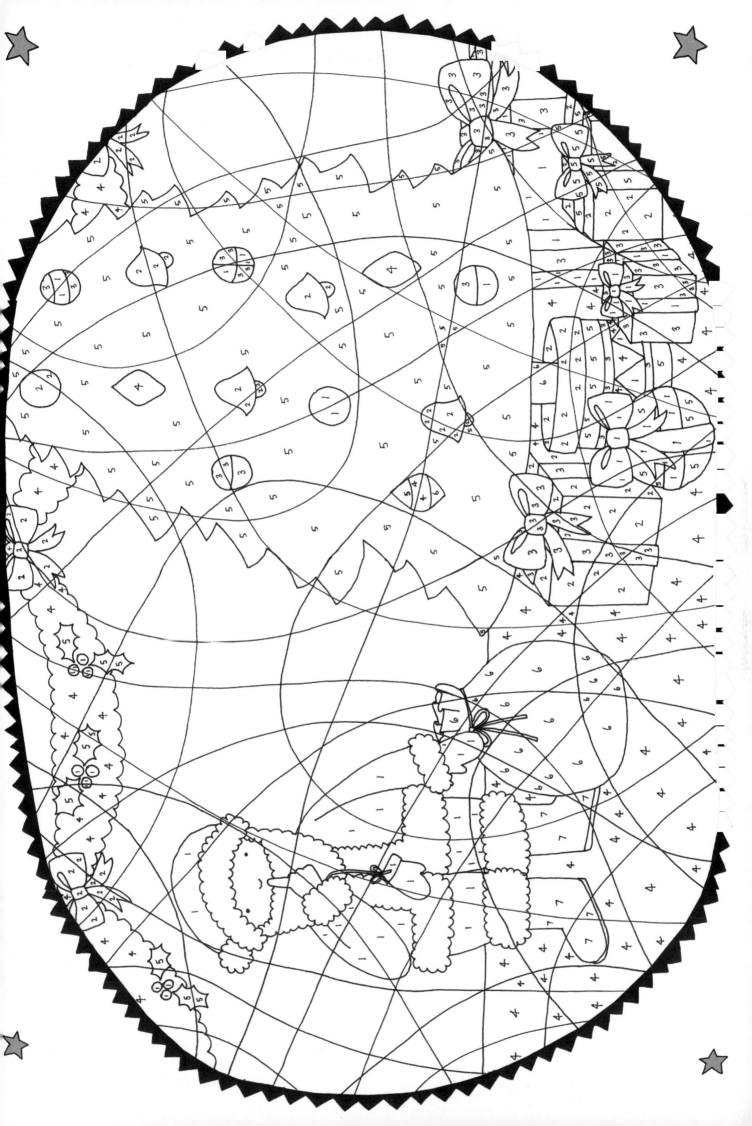

SKATER SKITTLES GAME...

Make this fabulous multi-player Skater Skittles game for your family and friends to enjoy.

HOW TO MAKE YOUR SKITTLES:

Simply cut out all the characters on the next two pages, not forgetting the small snip at the bottom of each character. Cut out the semi circles and slot them into the character bases to stand them up. Strengthen the bases with a little sticky tape.

Rip out the three strips of paper on the next page and scrunch up. These are going to be the balls. Stand all the characters in a triangle type shape, pointing towards you. You are now ready to play!

HOW TO PLAY:

Taking turns, stand around two metres away from your characters and roll the balls to try and knock them over. You have three balls per turn to do this.

Count how many characters you knocked over at the end of your turn and note it down. Stand up the characters again. It is now the next player's turn.

Each player gets five turns and the player who knocks down the most characters in total WINS!

Ball one

Ball two

Ball three

TREE TREAT BASKETS

Make these super Tree Treat Baskets out of this page. They are perfect to hang on your Christmas tree and overfill with delicious treats.

BASKET HANGING TABS 1 AND 2

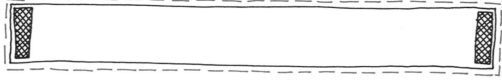

BASKET CUP 1

BASKET CUP 2

HOW TO MAKE THE BASKETS:

Decorate both sides of the basket cup and tabs. Then cut out along the pink dashed lines.

 Take one of your beautifully decorated basket cups and add a little glue to the outer shaded area tab. Curve the tab around and stick it onto the inner hatched area to create a cone shape.

 Take one of the hanging tabs and add a little glue to both shaded areas. Stick one end to the inside edge of your basket and the other end to the other inside edge. Use the hatched areas on the cup as a guide to do this. Leave to dry.

Fill up your cup with lots of tasty treats and hang on the Christmas tree.

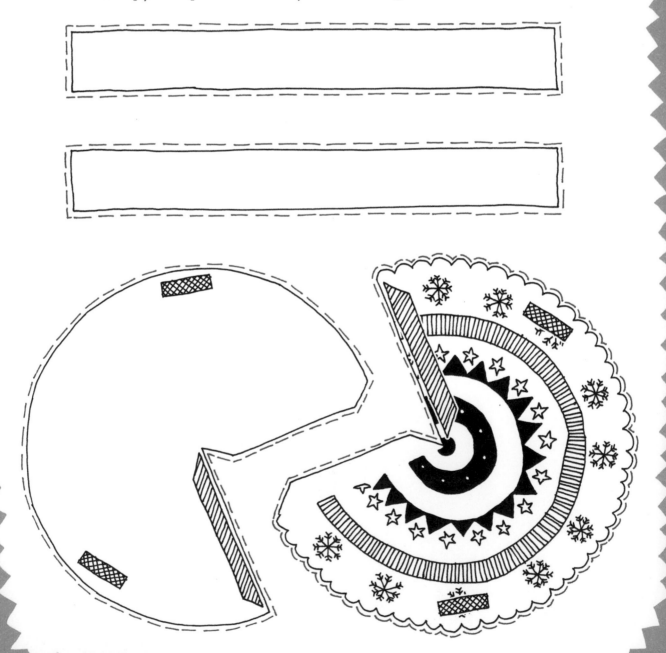

Make a magnificent ORIGAMI ⟩STAR⟨ out of this page ...

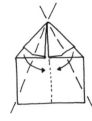

1. Fold one rectangle in half, each way. Unfold.

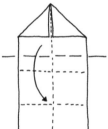

2. Fold the left edge to the centre crease. Unfold.

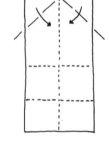

3. Fold in the two right corners to sit along the long centre crease.

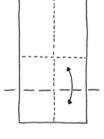

4. Fold the pointed edge over to the far-left crease.

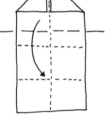

5. Flip over the paper and fold in the two right corners to the long centre crease.

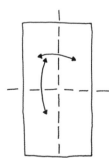

6. Now fold in the outer edges to the centre crease.

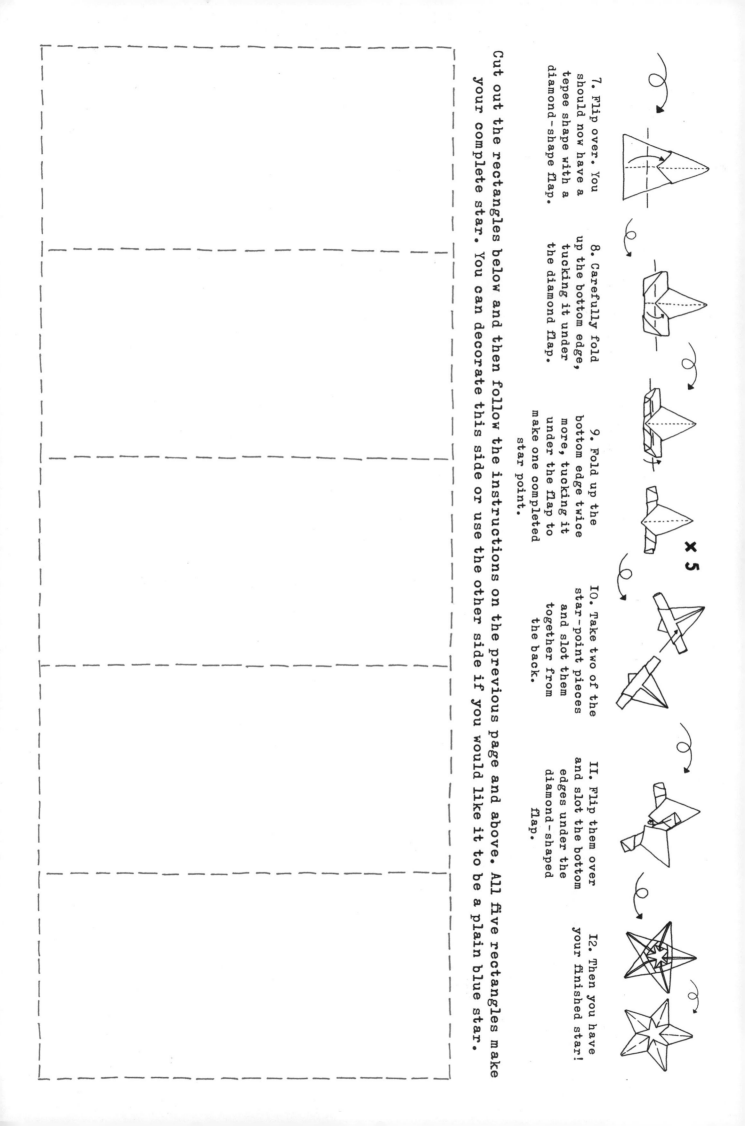

7. Flip over. You should now have a tepee shape with a diamond-shape flap.

8. Carefully fold up the bottom edge, tucking it under the diamond flap.

9. Fold up the bottom edge twice more, tucking it under the flap to make one completed star point.

x 5

10. Take two of the star-point pieces and slot them edges under the diamond-shaped flap.

11. Flip them over and slot the bottom edges under the diamond-shaped flap.

12. Then you have your finished star!

Cut out the rectangles below and then follow the instructions on the previous page and above. All five rectangles make your complete star. You can decorate this side or use the other side if you would like it to be a plain blue star.